How many altogether?

How many altogether?

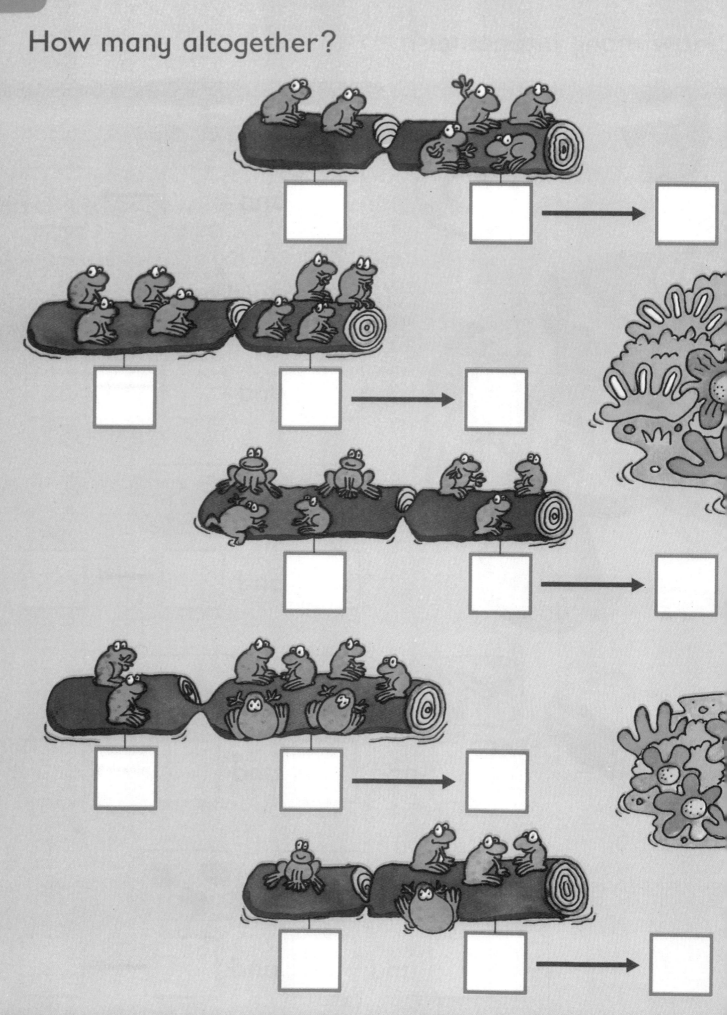

1

Addition to 10

Name

How many altogether?

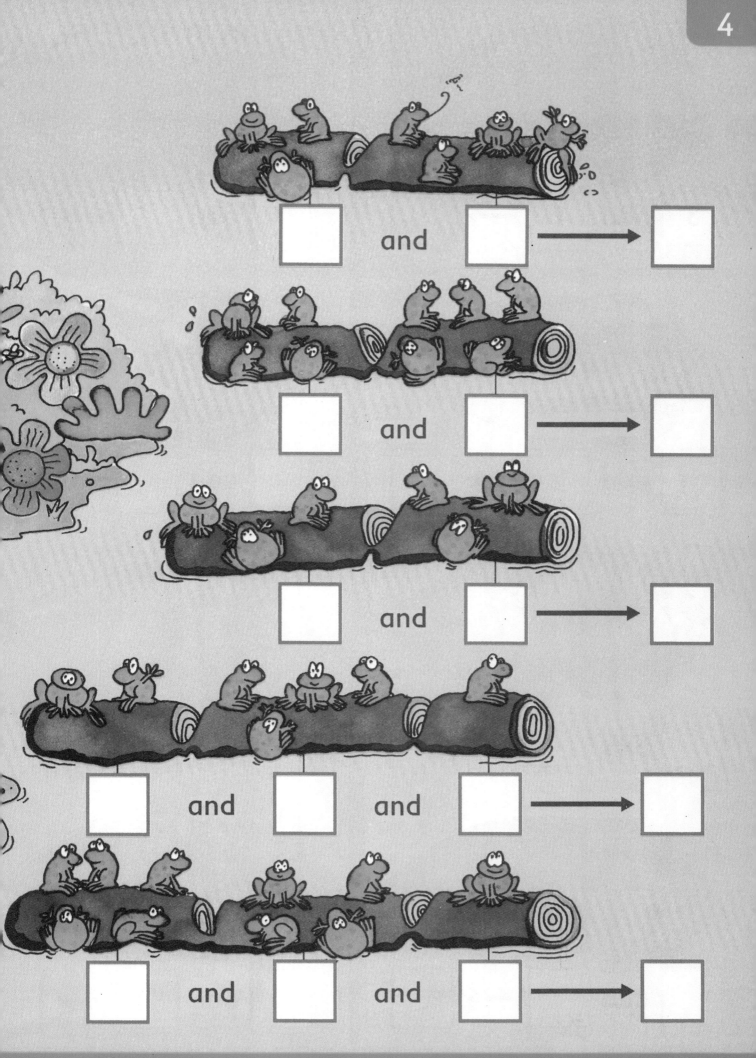

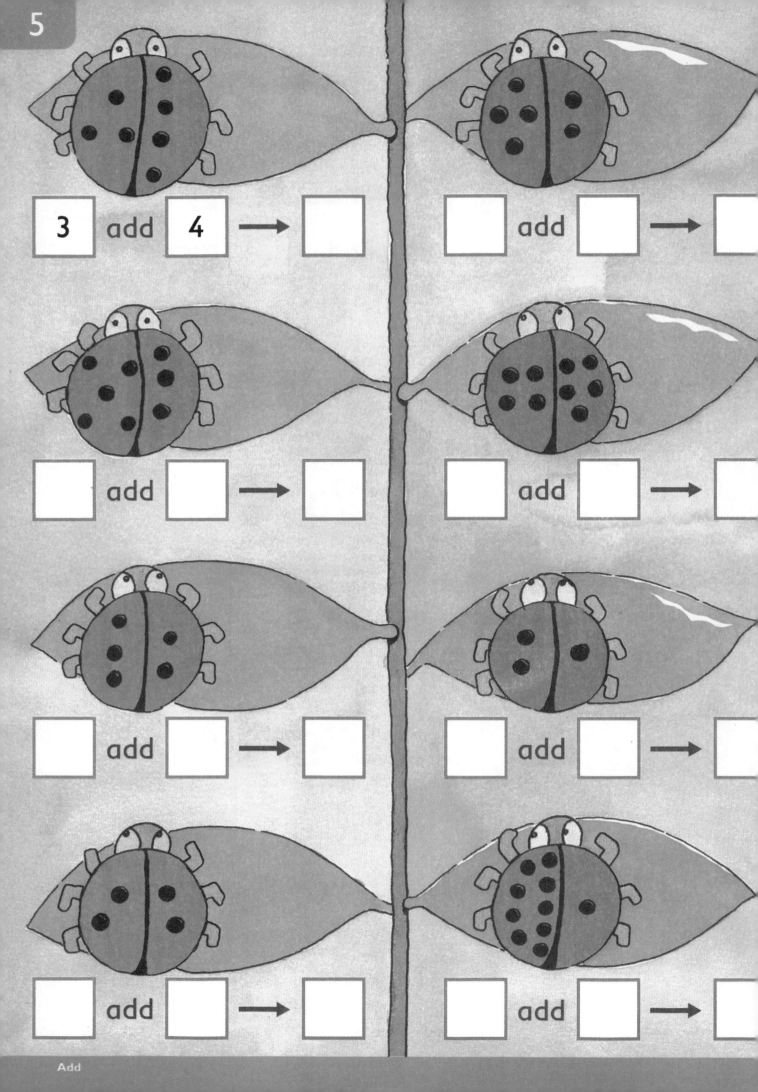

3 add 4 →

add →

add →

add →

add →

add →

add →

add →

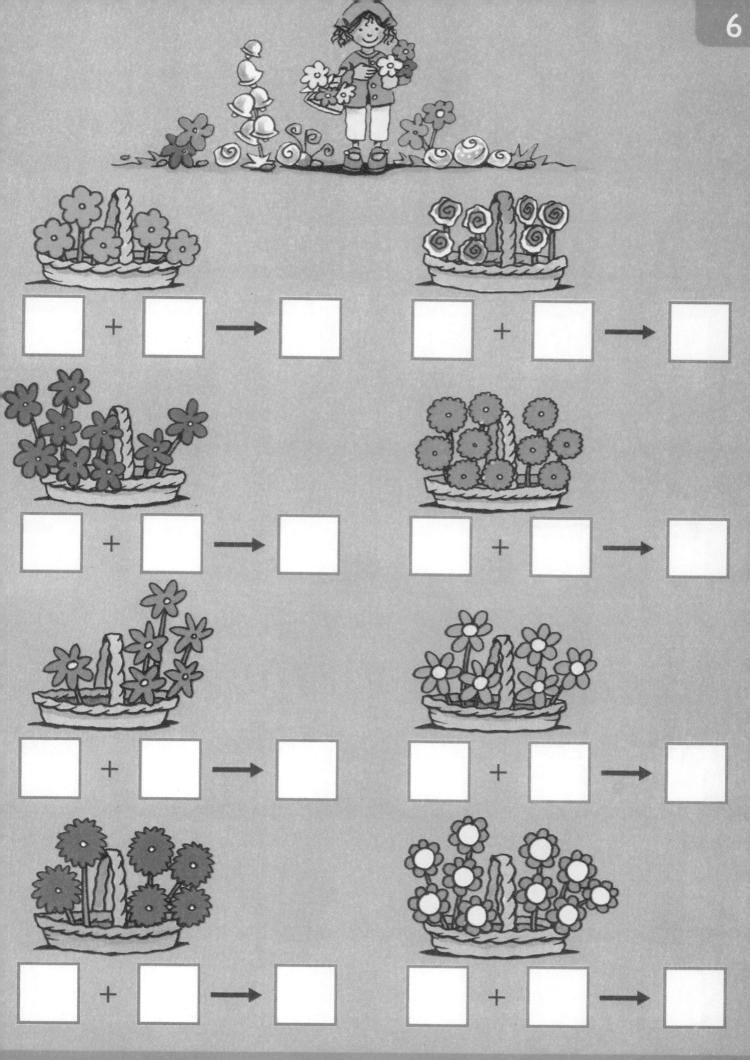

Draw 1 more.

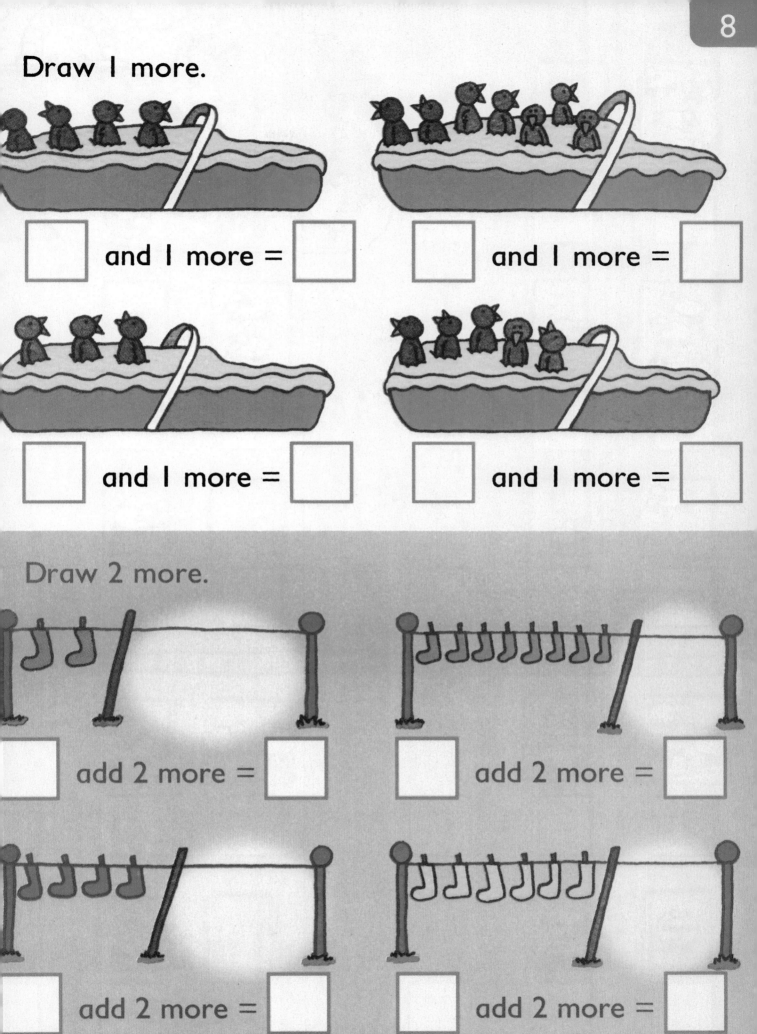

☐ and 1 more = ☐   ☐ and 1 more = ☐

☐ and 1 more = ☐   ☐ and 1 more = ☐

Draw 2 more.

☐ add 2 more = ☐   ☐ add 2 more = ☐

☐ add 2 more = ☐   ☐ add 2 more = ☐

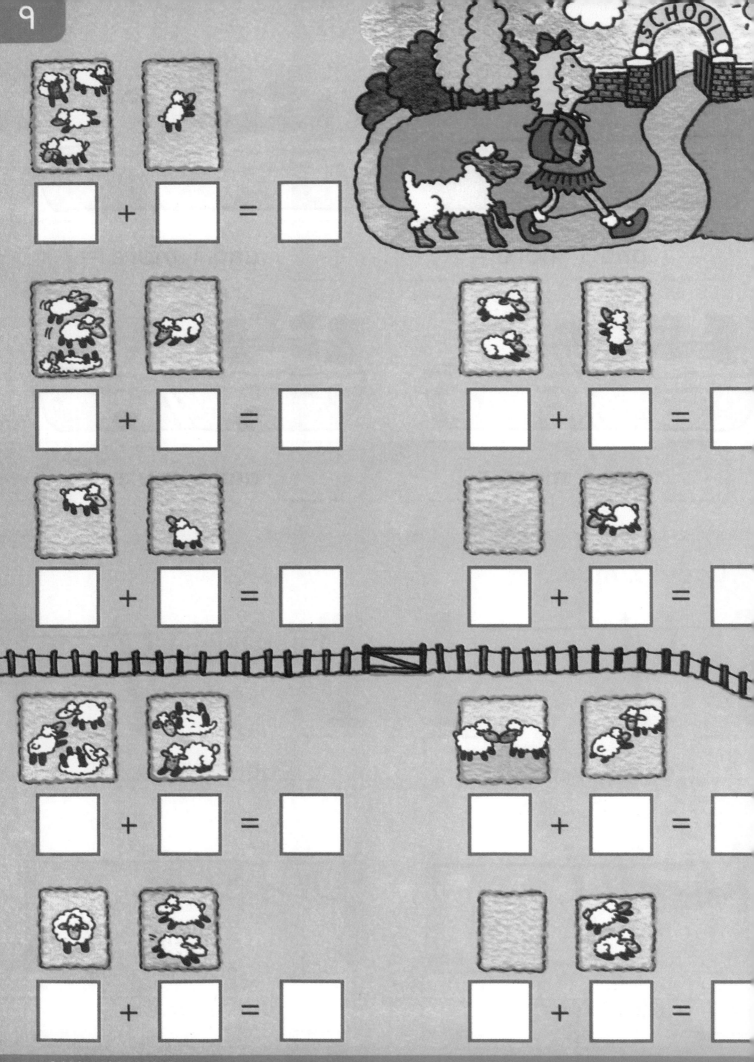

□ + □ = □

□ + □ = □   □ + □ = □

□ + □ = □   □ + □ = □

□ + □ = □   □ + □ = □

□ + □ = □   □ + □ = □

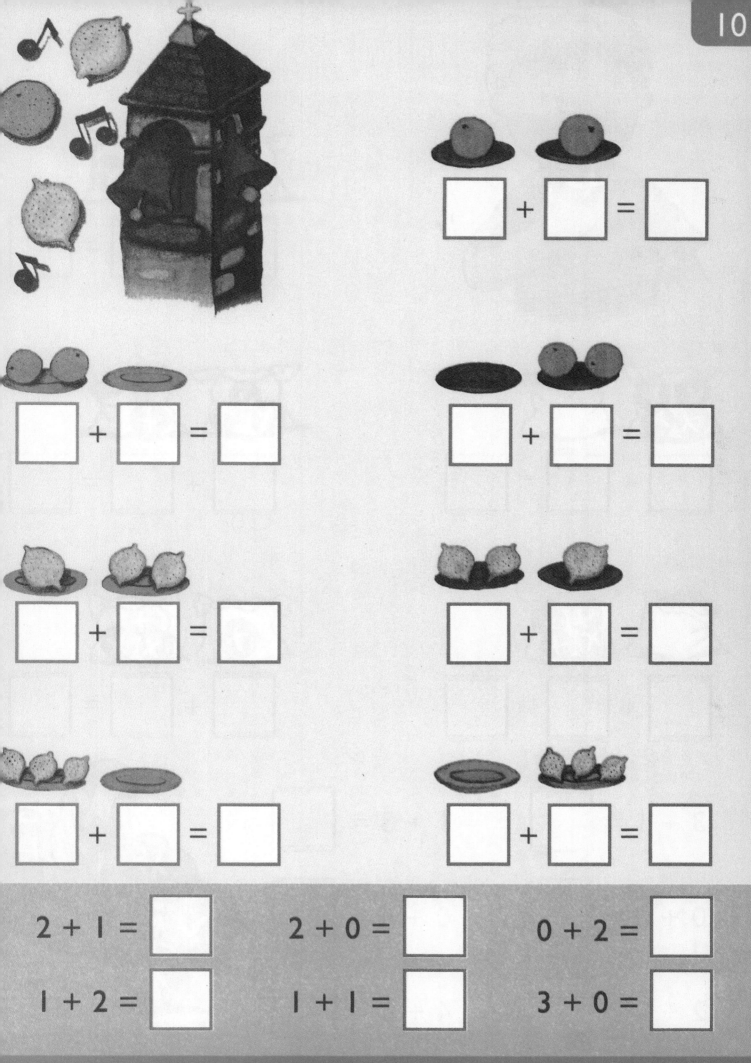

$$\boxed{} + \boxed{} = \boxed{}$$

$$\boxed{} + \boxed{} = \boxed{}$$

$$\boxed{} + \boxed{} = \boxed{}$$

$$\boxed{} + \boxed{} = \boxed{}$$

$$\boxed{} + \boxed{} = \boxed{}$$

$$\boxed{} + \boxed{} = \boxed{}$$

$$\boxed{} + \boxed{} = \boxed{}$$

$$2 + 1 = \boxed{} \qquad 2 + 0 = \boxed{} \qquad 0 + 2 = \boxed{}$$

$$1 + 2 = \boxed{} \qquad 1 + 1 = \boxed{} \qquad 3 + 0 = \boxed{}$$

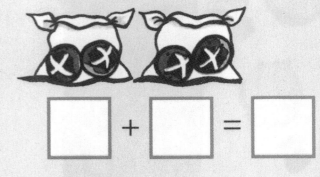

□ + □ = □

□ + □ = □

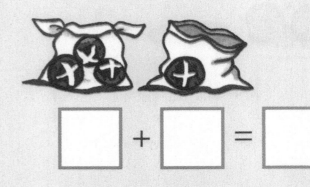

□ + □ = □

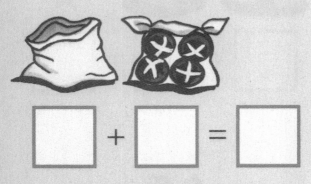

□ + □ = □

□ + □ = □

3 + 1 = □   1 + 3 = □

0 + 3 = □   0 + 4 = □

2 + 2 = □   4 + 0 = □

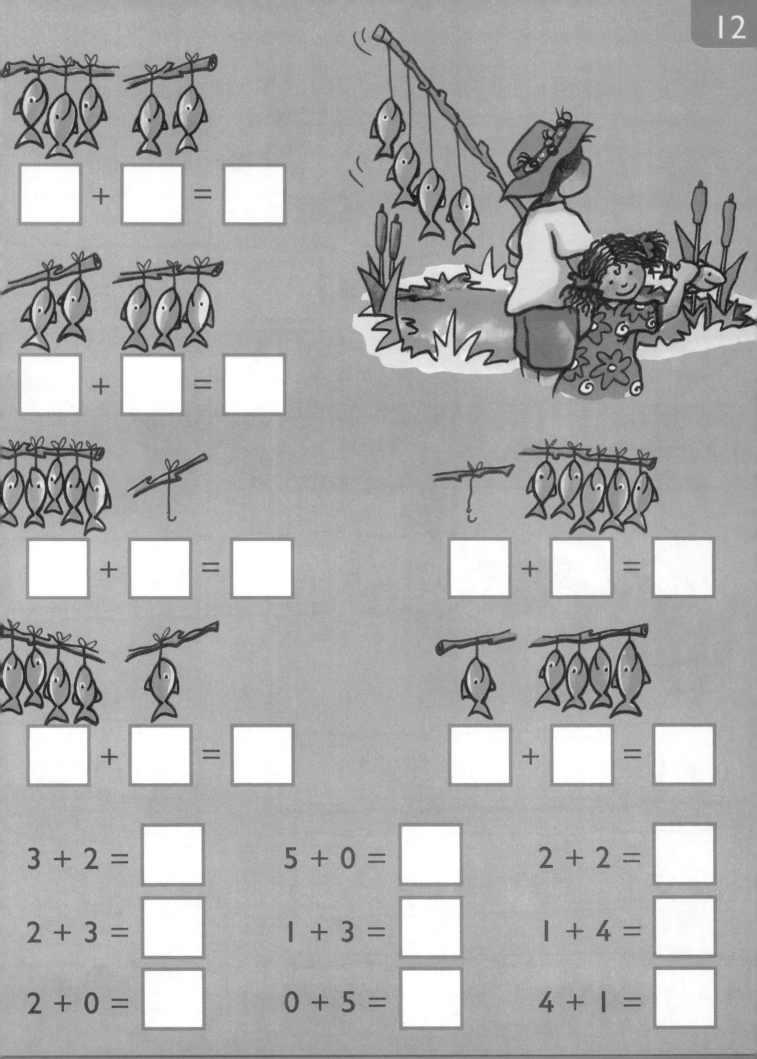

☐ + ☐ = ☐

☐ + ☐ = ☐

☐ + ☐ = ☐   ☐ + ☐ = ☐

☐ + ☐ = ☐   ☐ + ☐ = ☐

$3 + 2 =$ ☐ $5 + 0 =$ ☐ $2 + 2 =$ ☐

$2 + 3 =$ ☐ $1 + 3 =$ ☐ $1 + 4 =$ ☐

$2 + 0 =$ ☐ $0 + 5 =$ ☐ $4 + 1 =$ ☐

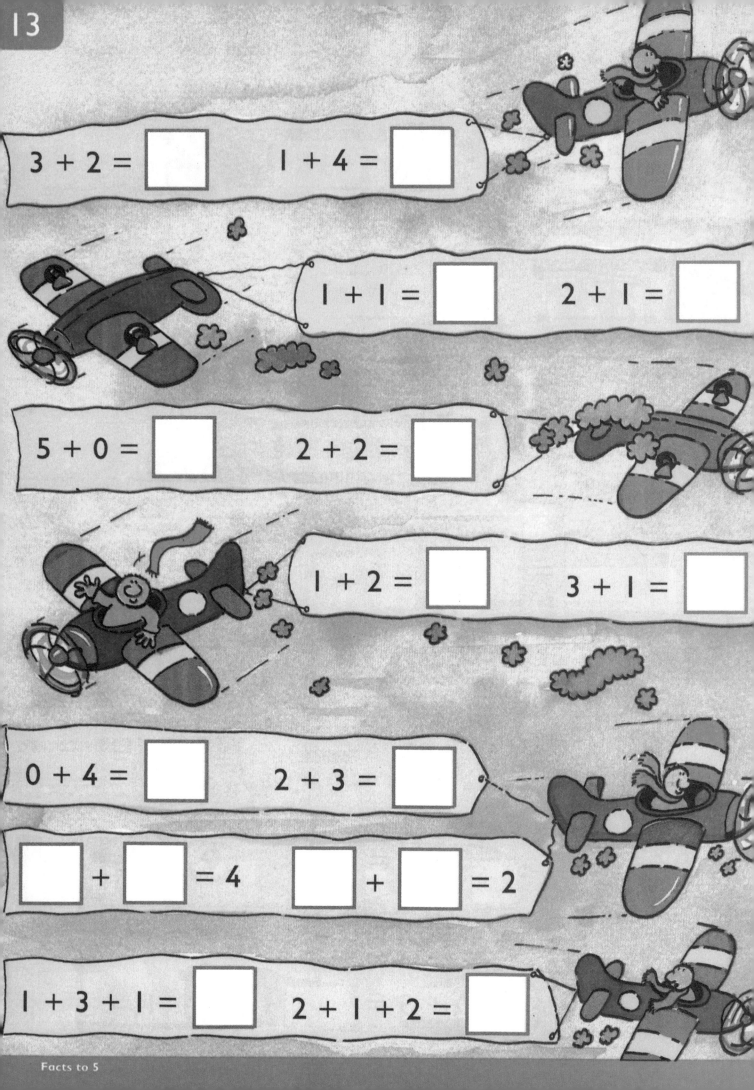

3 + 2 = ☐   1 + 4 = ☐

1 + 1 = ☐   2 + 1 = ☐

5 + 0 = ☐   2 + 2 = ☐

1 + 2 = ☐   3 + 1 = ☐

0 + 4 = ☐   2 + 3 = ☐

☐ + ☐ = 4   ☐ + ☐ = 2

1 + 3 + 1 = ☐   2 + 1 + 2 = ☐

1 How many altogether?

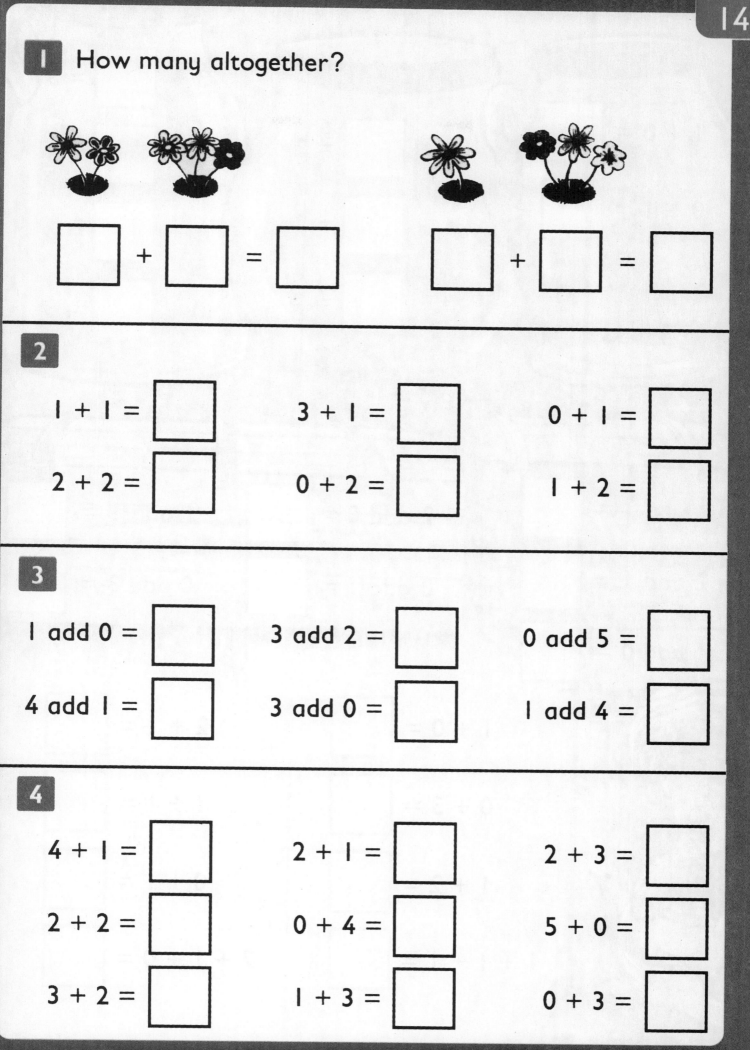

$\boxed{} + \boxed{} = \boxed{}$ $\boxed{} + \boxed{} = \boxed{}$

2

$1 + 1 = \boxed{}$ $3 + 1 = \boxed{}$ $0 + 1 = \boxed{}$

$2 + 2 = \boxed{}$ $0 + 2 = \boxed{}$ $1 + 2 = \boxed{}$

3

1 add $0 = \boxed{}$ 3 add $2 = \boxed{}$ 0 add $5 = \boxed{}$

4 add $1 = \boxed{}$ 3 add $0 = \boxed{}$ 1 add $4 = \boxed{}$

4

$4 + 1 = \boxed{}$ $2 + 1 = \boxed{}$ $2 + 3 = \boxed{}$

$2 + 2 = \boxed{}$ $0 + 4 = \boxed{}$ $5 + 0 = \boxed{}$

$3 + 2 = \boxed{}$ $1 + 3 = \boxed{}$ $0 + 3 = \boxed{}$

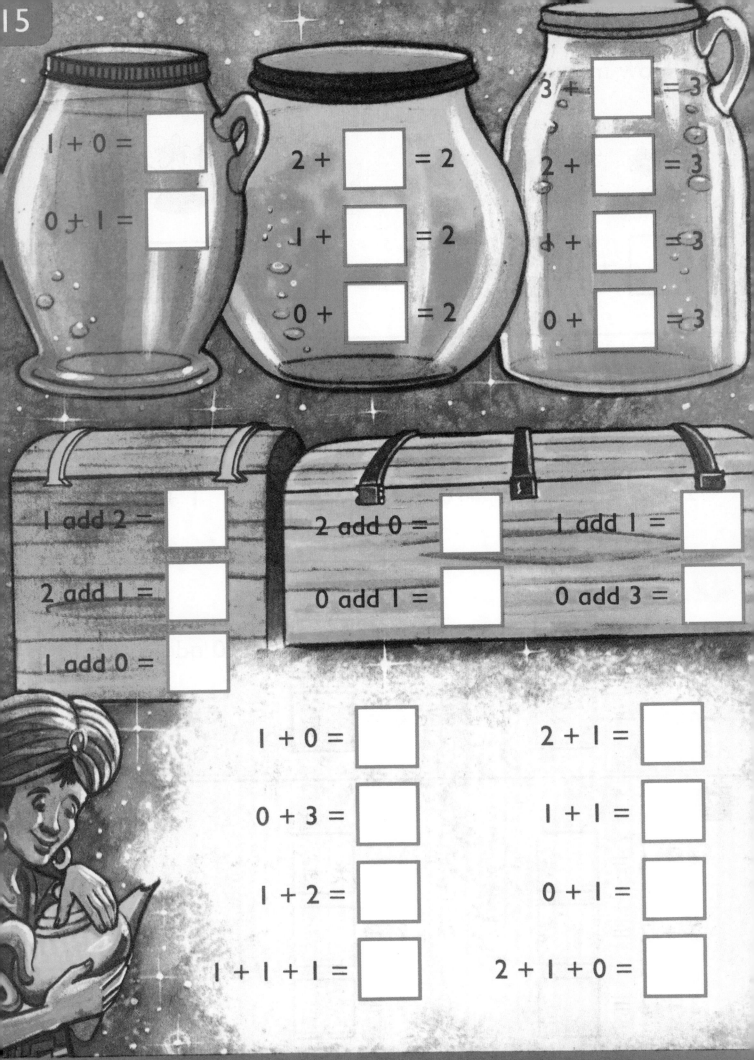

1 + 0 =

0 + 1 =

2 + □ = 2

1 + □ = 2

0 + □ = 2

3 + □ = 3

2 + □ = 3

1 + □ = 3

0 + □ = 3

1 add 2 =

2 add 1 =

1 add 0 =

2 add 0 =

0 add 1 =

1 add 1 =

0 add 3 =

1 + 0 =

0 + 3 =

1 + 2 =

1 + 1 + 1 =

2 + 1 =

1 + 1 =

0 + 1 =

2 + 1 + 0 =

Make 4.

4 + ☐

3 + ☐

2 + ☐

1 + ☐

0 + ☐

Make 5.

☐ + 5

☐ + 4

☐ + 3

☐ + 2

☐ + 1

☐ + 0

1 and 3 = ☐   3 add 2 = ☐   5 + 0 = ☐

2 add 2 = ☐   2 add 3 = ☐   3 + 1 = ☐

☐ + 2 = 4   1 + ☐ = 5

☐ + 0 = 4   2 + ☐ = 5

☐ + 4 = 4   4 + ☐ = 5

Draw and add.

1 and 1

$$1 + 1 = 2$$

2 and 2

$$\boxed{} + \boxed{} = \boxed{}$$

3 and 3

$$\boxed{} + \boxed{} = \boxed{}$$

4 and 4

$$\boxed{} + \boxed{} = \boxed{}$$

5 and 5

$$\boxed{} + \boxed{} = \boxed{}$$

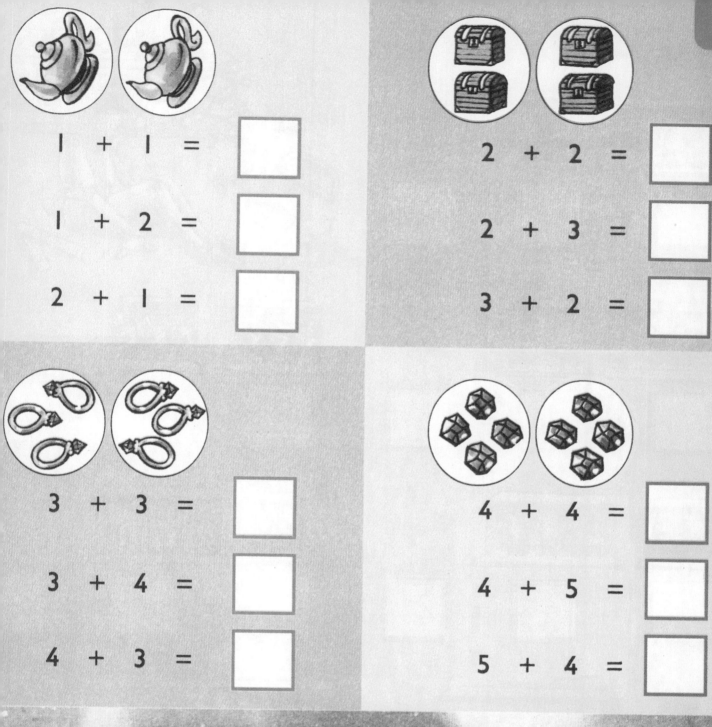

1 + 1 = ☐

1 + 2 = ☐

2 + 1 = ☐

2 + 2 = ☐

2 + 3 = ☐

3 + 2 = ☐

3 + 3 = ☐

3 + 4 = ☐

4 + 3 = ☐

4 + 4 = ☐

4 + 5 = ☐

5 + 4 = ☐

2 + 3 = ☐

3 + 4 = ☐

3 + 2 = ☐

5 + 4 = ☐

4 + 5 = ☐

2 + 1 = ☐

4 + 3 = ☐

1 + 2 = ☐

5 + 5 = ☐

5 + 6 = ☐

6 + 5 = ☐

Doubles, near doubles

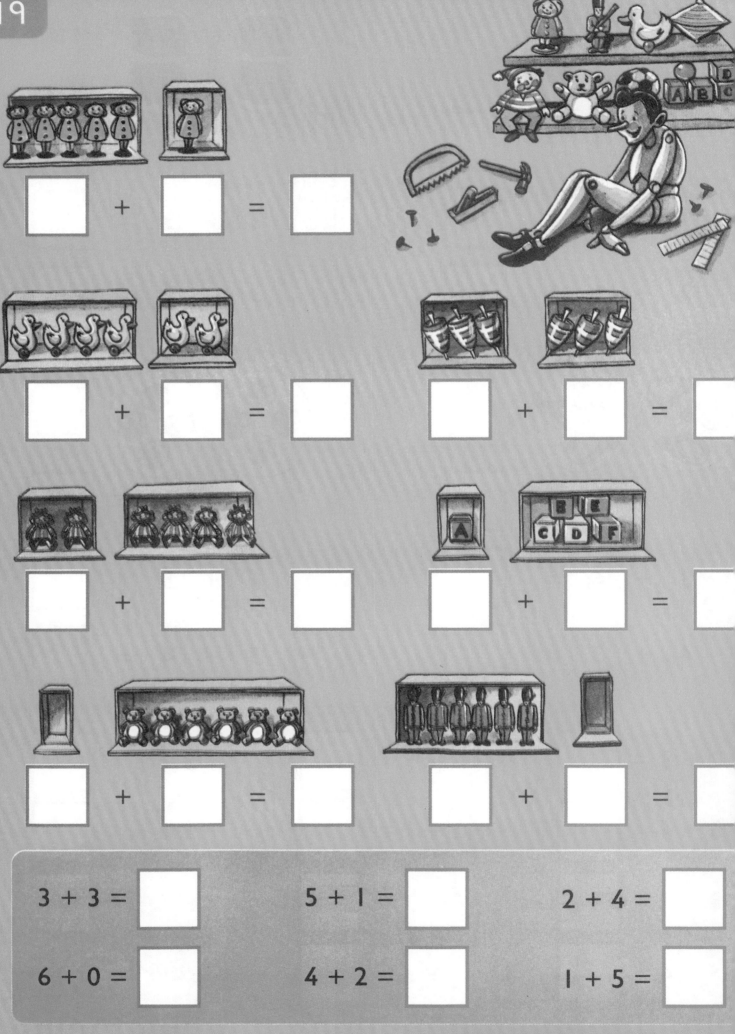

☐ + ☐ = ☐

☐ + ☐ = ☐   ☐ + ☐ = ☐

☐ + ☐ = ☐   ☐ + ☐ = ☐

☐ + ☐ = ☐   ☐ + ☐ = ☐

$3 + 3 =$ ☐ $5 + 1 =$ ☐ $2 + 4 =$ ☐

$6 + 0 =$ ☐ $4 + 2 =$ ☐ $1 + 5 =$ ☐

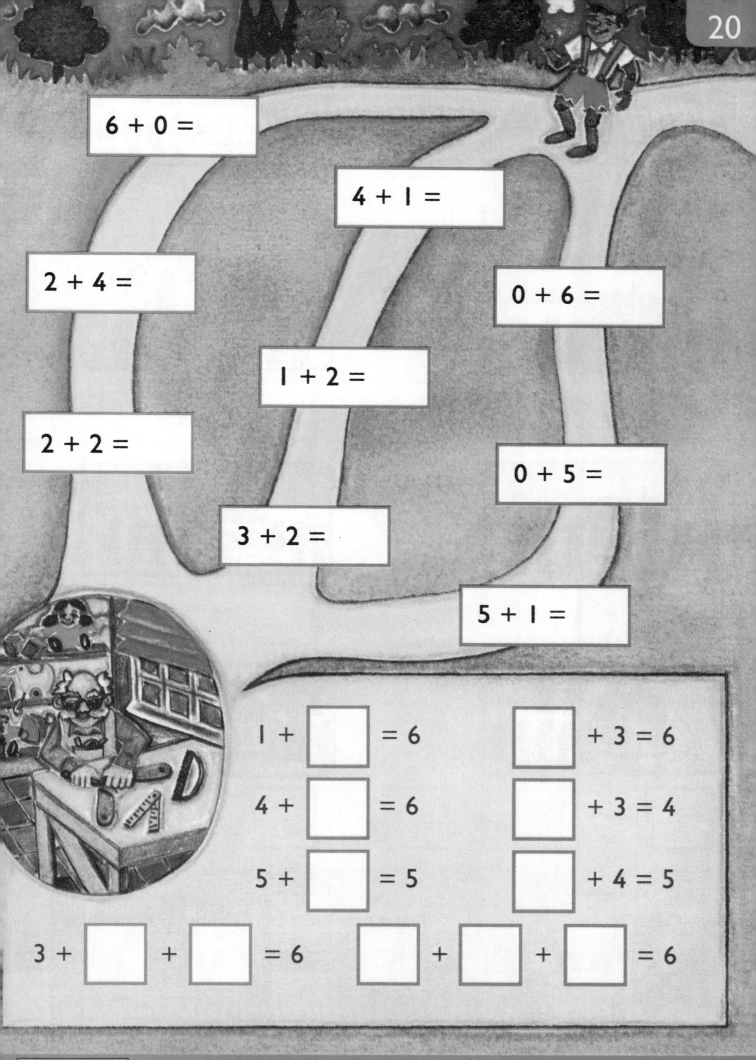

6 + 0 =

4 + 1 =

2 + 4 =

0 + 6 =

1 + 2 =

2 + 2 =

0 + 5 =

3 + 2 =

5 + 1 =

1 + ☐ = 6   ☐ + 3 = 6

4 + ☐ = 6   ☐ + 3 = 4

5 + ☐ = 5   ☐ + 4 = 5

3 + ☐ + ☐ = 6   ☐ + ☐ + ☐ = 6

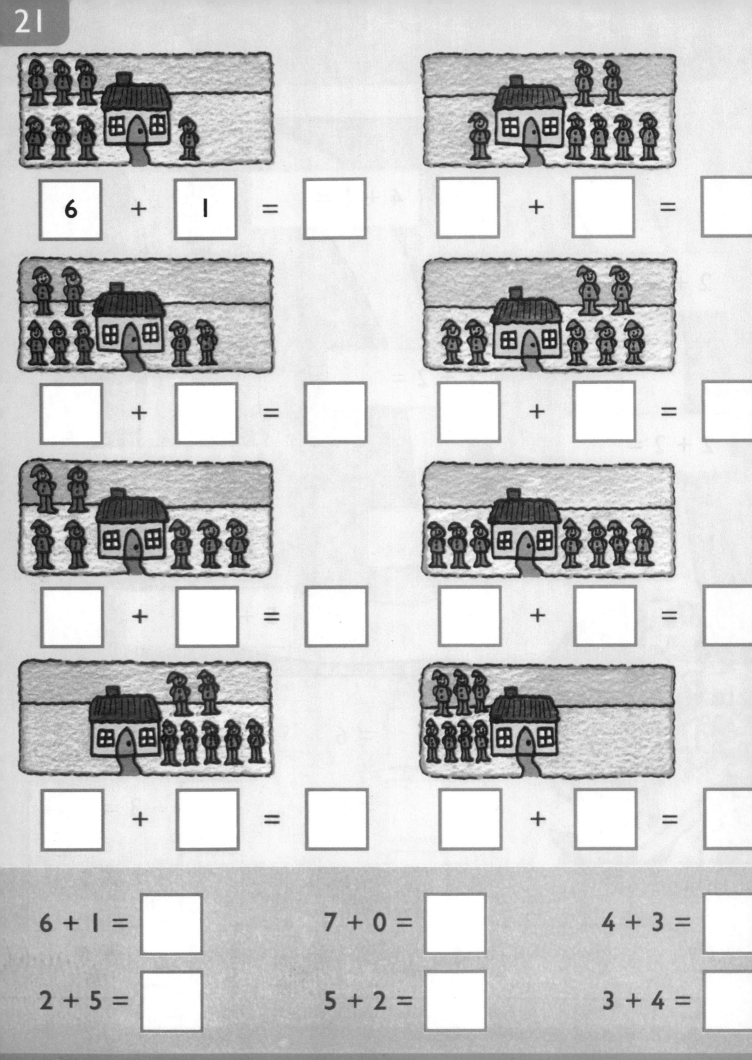

6 + 1 =

+ =

+ =

+ =

+ =

+ =

+ =

6 + 1 =   7 + 0 =   4 + 3 =

2 + 5 =   5 + 2 =   3 + 4 =

4 + 3 =

6 + 0 =

1 + 6 =

5 + 2 =

1 + 5 =

3 add 4 =

5 add 1 =

1 add 4 =

2 add 5 =

3 add 2 =

7 add 0 =

2 add 4 =

6 + 1 =

Make 7.

☐ + ☐

☐ + ☐ + ☐

☐ + ☐

☐ + ☐ + ☐

Snow White

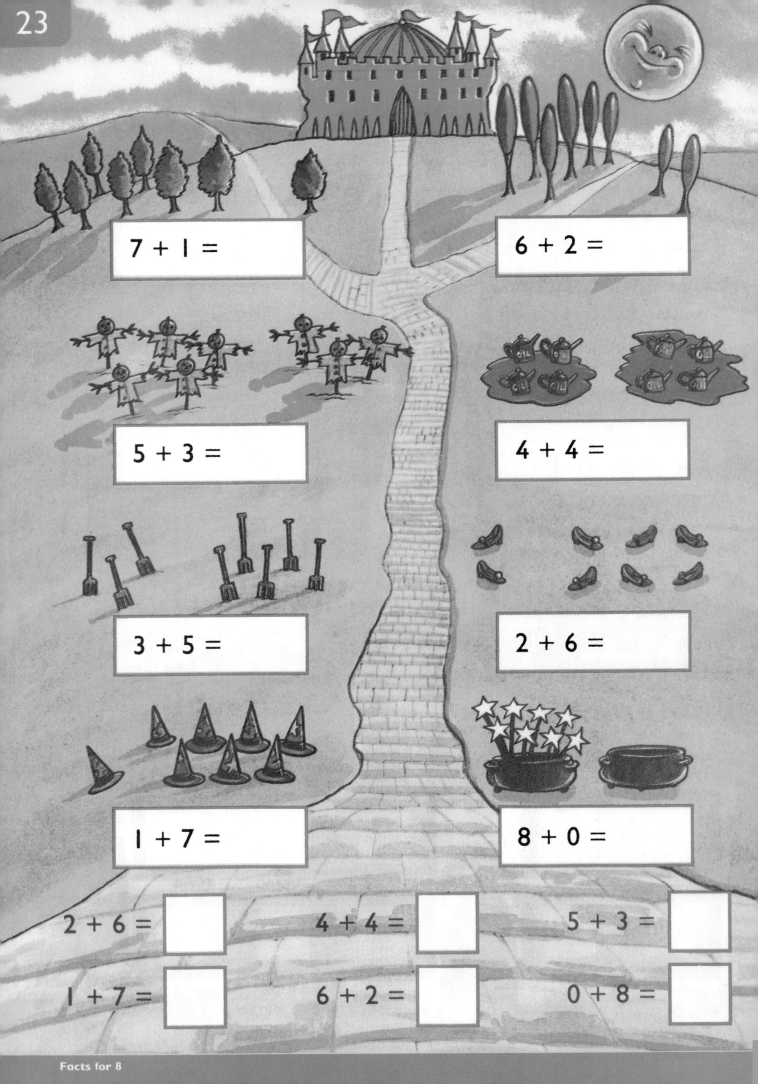

7 + 1 =

6 + 2 =

5 + 3 =

4 + 4 =

3 + 5 =

2 + 6 =

1 + 7 =

8 + 0 =

2 + 6 =

4 + 4 =

5 + 3 =

1 + 7 =

6 + 2 =

0 + 8 =

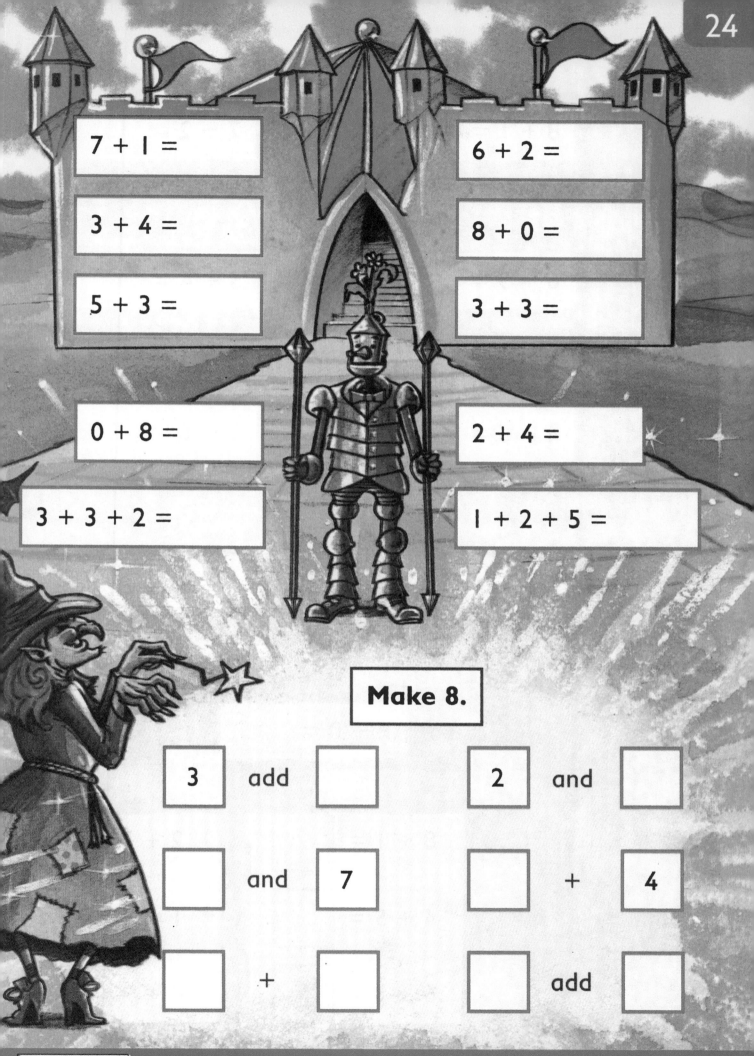

7 + 1 =

6 + 2 =

3 + 4 =

8 + 0 =

5 + 3 =

3 + 3 =

0 + 8 =

2 + 4 =

3 + 3 + 2 =

1 + 2 + 5 =

Make 8.

| 3 | add | | | 2 | and | |

| | and | 7 | | | + | 4 |

| | + | | | | add | |

8 + 1 =

7 + 2 =

6 + 3 =

5 + 4 =

4 + 5 =

3 + 6 =

2 + 7 =

1 + 8 =

9 + 0 =

8 + 1 =

2 + 7 =

4 + 5 =

1 + 8 =

6 + 3 =

0 + 9 =

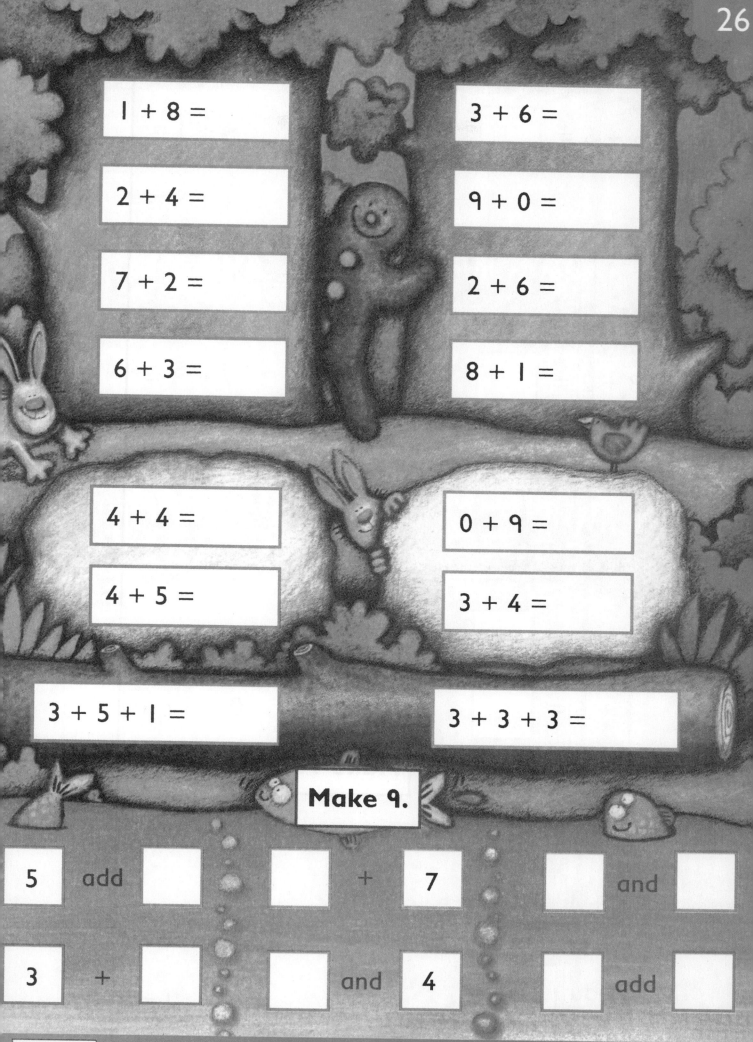

$1 + 8 =$

$3 + 6 =$

$2 + 4 =$

$9 + 0 =$

$7 + 2 =$

$2 + 6 =$

$6 + 3 =$

$8 + 1 =$

$4 + 4 =$

$0 + 9 =$

$4 + 5 =$

$3 + 4 =$

$3 + 5 + 1 =$

$3 + 3 + 3 =$

Make 9.

| 5 | add | | | + | 7 | | and | |

| 3 | + | | | and | 4 | | add | |

5 + 5 = ☐

9 + 1 = ☐

1 + 9 = ☐

8 + 2 = ☐

2 + 8 = ☐

7 + 3 = ☐

3 + 7 = ☐

6 + 4 = ☐

4 + 6 = ☐

10 + 0 = ☐

0 + 10 = ☐

Make 10.

2 and ☐

5 add ☐

☐ + 1

☐ and 4

3 add ☐

0 + ☐

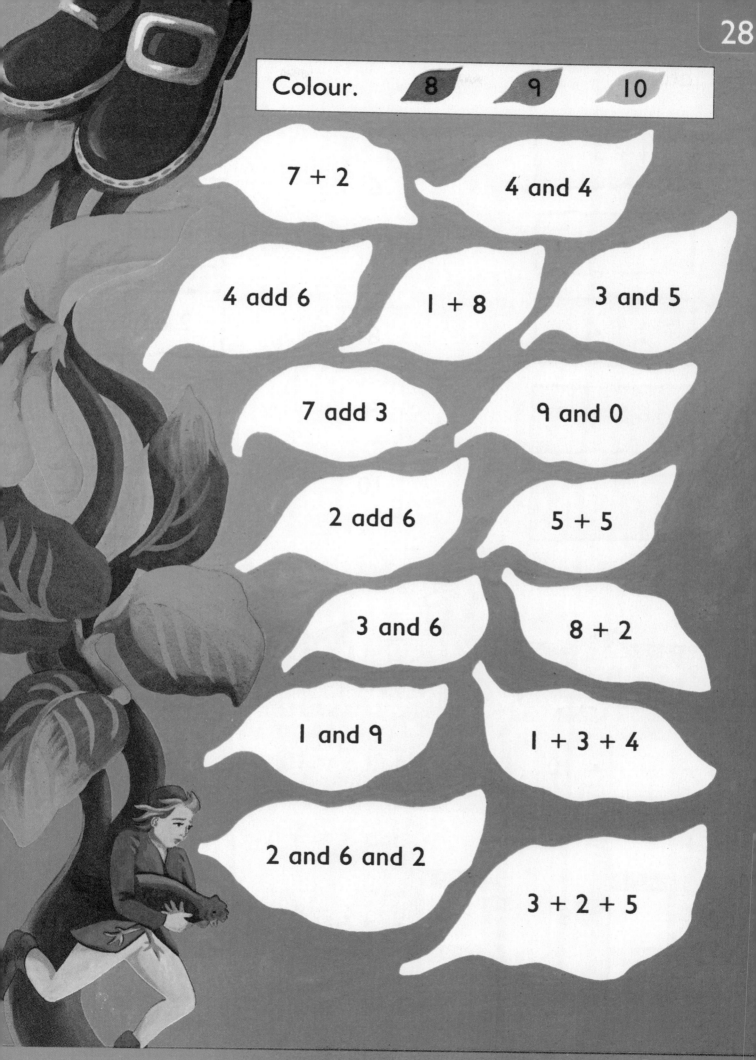

Colour. 8 9 10

7 + 2

4 and 4

4 add 6

1 + 8

3 and 5

7 add 3

9 and 0

2 add 6

5 + 5

3 and 6

8 + 2

1 and 9

1 + 3 + 4

2 and 6 and 2

3 + 2 + 5

Match.

3 + 3		6		5 and 2
4 + 3		7		6 add 3
2 + 4		8		2 add 7
9 + 1		9		0 and 8
3 + 5		10		8 and 2

6 + ☐ = 10

4 + ☐ = 9

2 + ☐ = 8

7 + ☐ = 7

☐ add 5 = 10

☐ and 8 = 9

☐ add 4 = 8

☐ and 3 = 10

☐ + ☐ = 9

☐ + ☐ = 1

1

3 + 1 =

4 + 2 =

9 + 1 =

8 + 2 =

5 + 1 =

6 + 2 =

2

3 + 7 =

2 + 8 =

4 + 5 =

9 + 0 =

4 + 3 =

3 + 2 =

1 + 7 =

6 + 3 =

5 + 4 =

3

3 add 3 =

4 add 6 =

0 add 4 =

5 add 3 =

7 add 2 =

1 add 1 =

4

How many altogether?

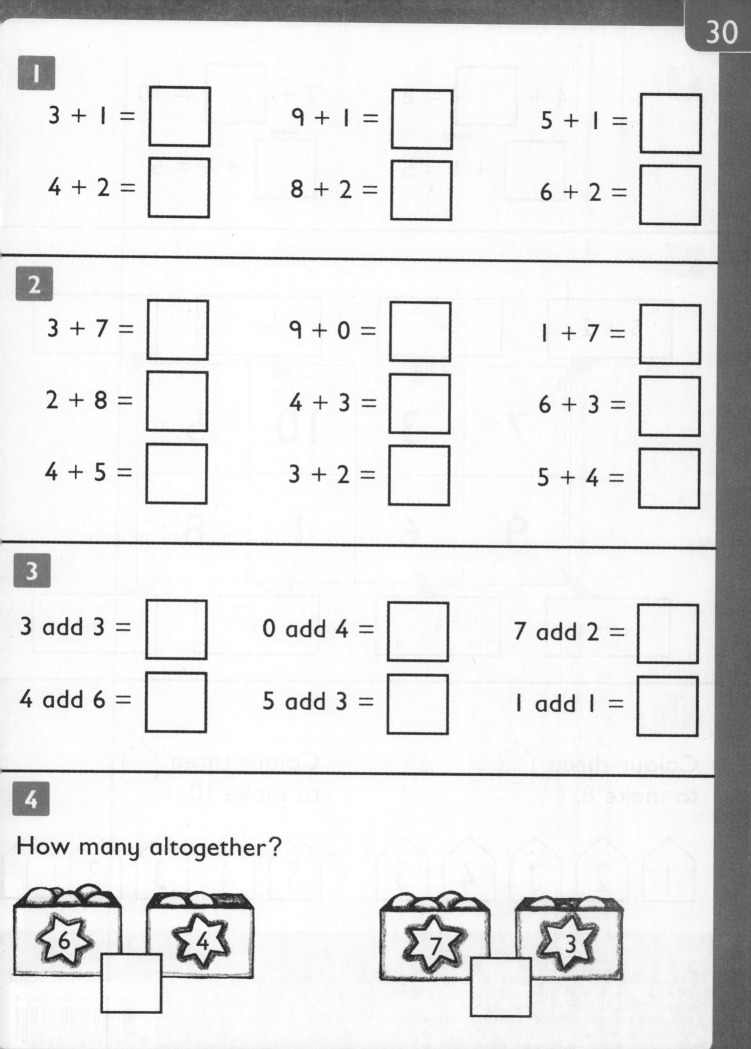

1

$4 + \boxed{} = 8$ $7 + \boxed{} = 10$

$\boxed{} + 1 = 5$ $\boxed{} + 4 = 6$

2

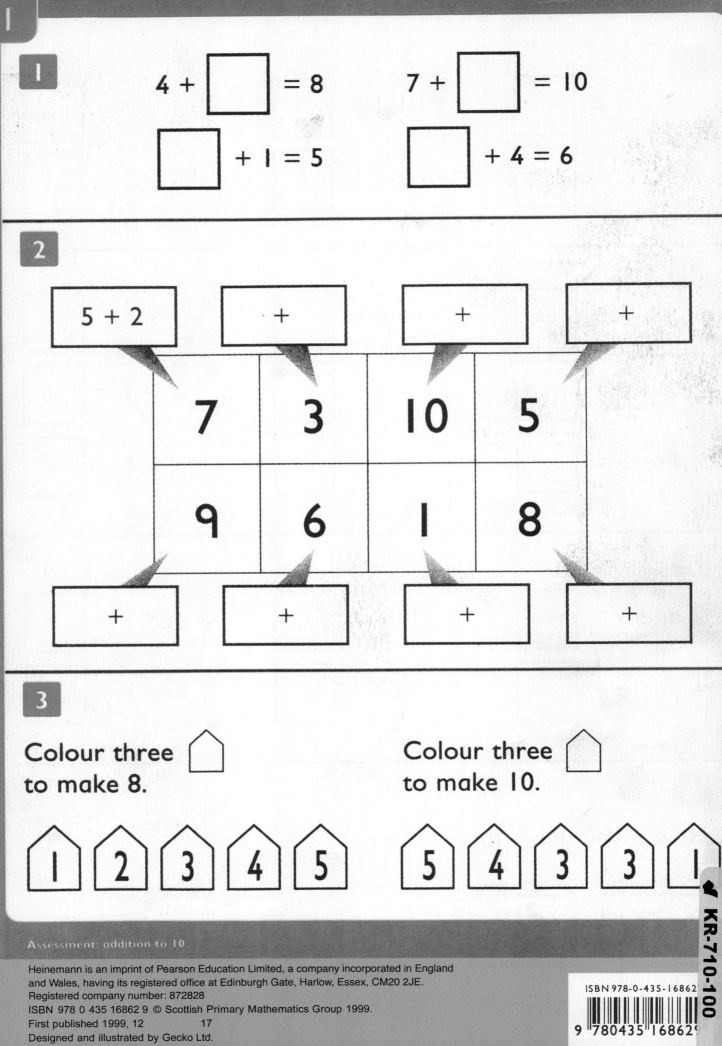

| 5 + 2 | + | + | + |

| 7 | 3 | 10 | 5 |
| 9 | 6 | 1 | 8 |

| + | + | + | + |

3

Colour three 🏠 to make 8.

| 1 | 2 | 3 | 4 | 5 |

Colour three 🏠 to make 10.

| 5 | 4 | 3 | 3 | 1 |

Assessment: addition to 10

Heinemann is an imprint of Pearson Education Limited, a company incorporated in England and Wales, having its registered office at Edinburgh Gate, Harlow, Essex, CM20 2JE.
Registered company number: 872828
ISBN 978 0 435 16862 9 © Scottish Primary Mathematics Group 1999.
First published 1999, 12   17
Designed and illustrated by Gecko Ltd.
Printed in Malaysia (CTP- VVP)

ISBN 978-0-435-16862
9 780435 168629
KR-710-100